POCKET

FC

The most common plant and animal fossils
of Europe described and illustrated in colour

Henry Gee, C. Fitzsimons & S. McCormick

TIME CHART

ERA	PERIOD		STAGE	AGE
CENOZOIC	Quaternary		Holocene (Recent) Pleistocene	
				2
	Tertiary		Pliocene Miocene Oligocene Eocene Palaeocene	
				65
MESOZOIC	Cretaceous		Maastrichtian Senonian Turonian Cenomanian Albian Aptian Neocomian: Barremian Hauterivian Valanginian Berriasian	
				135
	Jurassic		Portlandian/ Volgian Kimmeridgian Oxfordian Callovian Bathonian Bajocian Lias: Toarcian Pliensbachian Sinemurian Hettangian	
				200
	Triassic			
				240

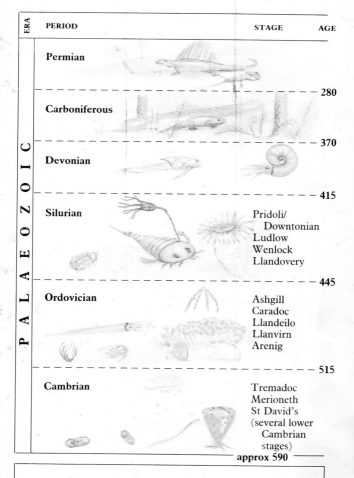

ERA	PERIOD	STAGE	AGE
	Permian		
			— 280
	Carboniferous		
			— 370
P A L A E O Z O I C	Devonian		
			— 415
	Silurian	Pridoli/ Downtonian Ludlow Wenlock Llandovery	
			— 445
	Ordovician	Ashgill Caradoc Llandeilo Llanvirn Arenig	
			— 515

	Cambrian	Tremadoc
		Merioneth
		St David's
		(several lower
		  Cambrian
		  stages)	

		approx 590	

AGES in the time chart are given in millions of years and are approximate.

NAMES and numbers of stages in each period are likely to vary from place to place.

POCKET REFERENCE GUIDES

FOSSILS

The most common plant and animal fossils
of Europe described and illustrated in colour

Henry Gee, C. Fitzsimons & S. McCormick

BROCKHAMPTON PRESS

Front cover illustration: Didymograptus, Trinucleus, Terebratula

This edition published in 1999 by
Brockhampton Press,
20 Bloomsbury Street,
London WC1B 3QA,
a member of the Hodder Headline Group.

This edition produced under licence by
Malcolm Saunders Publishing Ltd, London

A CIP Catalogue record for this book is available from the British Library

Title: Pocket Reference Guides, FOSSILS
ISBN: 1 86019 781 7

Printed in China by Colorcraft

Contents

Introduction

Fossils are the mineralized remains of long-dead animals and plants, and can be beautiful objects as well as fascinating hints of the riotous diversity and profusion of life long ago. This book is intended for those curious about the fossils they pick up on the beach after storms, in road or railway cuttings or in quarries. In it we have described and illustrated many of the most common fossils to be found in Europe, with details of their geological ages and where you can expect to find them. Some of the terms we use to describe the fossils may be unfamiliar, so we have included a glossary and a chart of the names and relative ages of the geological strata.

Collecting the fossils in one's own neighbourhood can be a rewarding pastime, and palaeontology is one of the few sciences in which the keen amateur can still make a vital contribution. Those in search of more information should contact their local museum, which will be pleased to provide more detailed information than can be squeezed into this pocket guide. When setting out on a fossil-hunting expedition, remember that many fossil-bearing localities are dangerous places. Wear heavy boots and a hard hat, and if unaccompanied, tell somebody where you are going and how long you expect to be away. At the site, take careful notes about the fossils and their locations as precisely as you can — this is important scientific information. If possible, take colour photographs. However you store or display your trophies at home, make sure each one has a label recording essential site details, and keep duplicate labels in a card index or on a personal computer. Fossils without information may look pretty but are scientifically useless.

Most importantly of all, **make sure you have written permission from the landowner to collect fossils on the site**. Many sites are on private land or owned by railway companies, quarry operators and so on. Some are protected sites of scientific interest and unauthorized collection may be forbidden. If in doubt, contact your local museum who should have information about local sites of interest.

How to use this book

We have divided this book into a number of colour-coded sections reflecting the classification of the animals and plants found as fossils. To identify your fossil, first decide the group to which it belongs using the *Guide to Identification* that follows. It is possible that you will not be able to find the exact fossil in this book, although you will probably find something like it, and get some idea about its broad zoological or botanical affinity.

Guide to identification

First decide the group to which your fossil belongs.

 PLANTS are hardly ever found complete as fossils, although leaves, fruits and fragments of wood, bark and stems are not uncommon. This makes identification extremely difficult, even for the specialist. Some plants have one Latin name for the leaves, another for the stems, yet a third for the roots. Some are even confused with plantlike animals such as bryozoans or graptolites.

 SPONGES & CORALS: sponges are simple marine animals known from well before the Cambrian period to the present day. Their varied shapes make them hard to identify positively. Their skeletons are made of a meshwork either of protein or of *calcareous* or *siliceous spicules*. These are useful clues to identification but are microscopic and fall outside the skills of most amateurs. **Archaeocyaths** are cup-shaped sponge-like animals known only from the Cambrian. Corals look a bit like sponges but are in fact colonial animals related to sea anemones. The corals preserved as fossils are the remains of the calcareous 'cups' secreted by each individual, or *polyp*. They are classified by the numbers and arrangements of partition walls or *septa* in each cup.

MOLLUSCS are by far the most important fossil group. Common from the Cambrian to the present day, the snails or **gastropods** have a single shell coiled in a helix or plane spiral. Unlike the cephalopod shell, it is not subdivided internally by septa.

 The **bivalve** body is encased in two valves, one on each side, joined along the back by a hinge. First recorded in the Middle Cambrian, they did not really come into their own until the Mesozoic and are abundant today.

 Cephalopods include the modern squid, octopi and nautilus, only the last of which retains an external shell. The cephalopod shell is subdivided internally by septa. Making their first appearance in the Chinese Middle Cambrian, **nautiloids** first appeared in Europe in any numbers in the Lower Ordovician, with **ammonoids** in the Upper Devonian. A tube or *siphuncle* runs down the middle of the nautiloid shell, connecting all the chambers. In ammonoids and one group of nautiloids it runs down one edge. Nautiloid shells usually have simple *suture* lines and, if coiled, a central perforation. Ammonoid shells generally lack this, but their suture lines range from simple zig-zags (in goniatites), zig-zags alternating with more complex *saddles* and *lobes* (ceratites) to very sinuous and complex shapes (ammonites). The rapid evolution, worldwide distribution and characteristic suturing of ammonites makes them superb *zone fossils* in the Mesozoic, especially the Jurassic. They died out in the Cretaceous.

9

ARTHROPODS, or joined-limbed animals, are the most abundant animals today and include insects, millipedes, centipedes, crustaceans, spiders, scorpions, mites and ticks. But the most important fossil arthropods are the **trilobites**, which appeared in profusion in the Cambrian and dominated the seas until their decline in the Carboniferous. They are not known after the end of the Permian. More than 1500 *genera* and thousands of species are known from all parts of the world. Rich trilobite pickings can be had in Sweden, Norway, Wales (Cambrian), Scotland (Ordovician), the west of England (Silurian), Russia, Bohemia, and parts of North Africa and North America. The trilobite body ranges in length from less than a millimetre to more than 75 centimetres, and is divided lengthwise into a head, *thorax* and tail, and sideways into three lobes (hence the name) like the nave and aisles of a church. The head has a central lobe or *glabella* with or without a pair of compound eyes, one on each side, and a front margin, sometimes extending towards the *genal angles* on the rear corners of the head.

BRYOZOA or 'moss animals' are exclusively colonial and are easily confused with corals and some kinds of graptolite. Important as fossils, they are usually found as low-growing patterns or encrustations on rock surfaces, but may form erect, branching colonies. Each cup or *theca* housed a tiny individual or *zooid*. There are four major groups of bryozoa: the **trepostomes**, **cryptostomes**, **cheilostomes** and **cyclostomes**. All are represented here but precise details of identification usually require the help of a specialist.

BRACHIOPODS are marine animals with two distinct but equilateral valves; a lower *pedicle valve* (usually the larger of the two) and an upper, *brachial valve*. The shells of the unrelated bivalve molluscs, in contrast, are lateral (left and right, rather than top and bottom) and are not usually equilateral. Living brachiopods attach themselves to a solid object by a fleshy stalk or *pedicle* emerging from the back of the shell; the *gape* is always at the front rather than underneath, as in bivalves. The animals feed by trapping particles in a coiled arrangement of tentacles called a *lophophore*, which is supported by a skeleton or *brachidium* that is sometimes preserved in fossils in various shapes that can aid identification; it may be arranged as a pair of simple 'horns' or *crura*, or in delicate spiral shapes. There are two major groups of brachiopod, the **inarticulates** with *chitinous* or *calcareous* valves held together by soft tissues; and the **articulates**, with calcareous valves hinged together by two teeth in the pedicle valve that fit into two sockets in the brachial valve. The hinge may run along the entire back edge of the brachial valve (*strophic*) or just pivot on a small part of it just under the beak like the silver lid in an antique wine decanter (*non-strophic*). The space between the beak and the hinge line is called the *interarea*; the gap in the pedicle valve between the hinge and the place where the pedicle emerges (the *pedicle foramen*) is called the *delthyrium*, and may be closed by a pair of small plates. The articulates comprise several important subgroups, the orthids, strophomenids, pentamerids, spiriferids, rhynchonellids and terebratulids, all of which are common as fossils. Fewer than 100 of the 3000 recorded genera of brachiopod survive today.

 ECHINODERMS, the spiny-skinned animals, have been important in the sea since the Lower Cambrian. Modern forms include starfish (asteroids), brittle-stars (ophiuroids), sea-urchins (echinoids), sea-cucumbers (holothurians) and sea-lilies and feather-stars (crinoids), although many other strange groups such as cystoids and blastoids have come and gone. All usually have a skeleton of calcite plates and a distinctive five-way symmetry, as well as a distinctive system of water tubes connected to mobile 'tube feet' arranged along a series of food grooves. The **crinoids** or sea-lilies are rare today but are very important as fossils from the Lower Ordovician upwards. The fragile **asteroids** and **ophiuroids** are generally rare as fossils but are locally abundant if conditions of preservation are just right.

 GRAPTOLITES were marine animals that lived in colonies made of a kind of protein, preserved in rocks as a black carbon film; they get their name from their resemblance to pencil markings. Each individual or *zooid* lived in a cup or *theca*, arranged in lines along one (*uniserial*), or both (*biserial*) sides of the blade-like *stipe*. There were two principal groups of graptolite: the bushy bottom-living **dendroids**, first to evolve in the mid-Cambrian and last to die out, in the late Carboniferous; and the free-floating **graptoloids**, common in the Ordovician, Silurian and lower Devonian. The graptoloids were very diverse and are extremely useful as zone fossils in the Ordovician and Silurian.

 The VERTEBRATES, or backboned animals, comprise the fishes, amphibians, reptiles, birds and mammals, including ourselves. Although the very earliest fishes appeared in the Late Cambrian, the fossil record of vertebrates is generally rather poor. Unless armoured with bony plates or scales, the bony skeleton of vertebrates is internal and tends to break up easily after death. For all that one hears and reads about dinosaurs, the most common (or least rare) vertebrate fossils are teeth. These are coated with enamel, the hardest substance produced by living organisms, and are thus resistant to damage. The rarest vertebrate species of all is our own, usually betrayed only by signs of activity, such as stone tools, rather than bones.

How fossils form

Far from being the actual remains of animals and plants that lived millions of years ago, fossils are impressions left when the dead bodies of creatures fell into sand, mud, volcanic ash or other soft materials and rotted away, leaving a hole which became filled with minerals percolating through the sediment. Millions of years of slow accumulation squeezed the soft sediment into rocks such as sandstone, limestone and shale. Animals with hard shells fossilize the best, and the best places to find fossils are sediments that formed on the seafloor. So the most common fossils are hard-shelled marine animals such as trilobites and molluscs. The rarest of all are backboned animals that lived on land, such as fossil **hominids**.

Making a positive identification

The fossils are organized into colour-coded sections, marked by symbols for each major group. Once you have found the right page, you will find details of the characteristic features of each fossil described in the first box, and notes on the stratigraphic position (see time chart on front endpapers) and geographical distribution in the second. More information about the evolution of the fossil form and its relatives can be found in the third box, whereas the fourth lists fossils that either look similar or may be related to the fossil in the main picture. Some pages illustrate a variety of common but related fossil forms.

Specimen page

Colour of band and symbol denotes major group

Genus of fossil

Name of subgroup

Colour illustration of characteristics

Primary identification features

Stratigraphy and distribution

Additional information

Similar and related forms

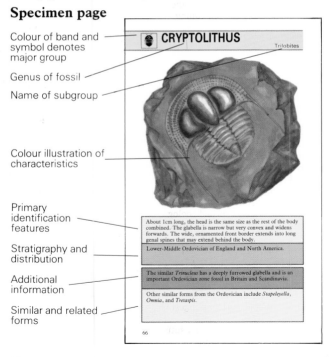

CRYPTOLITHUS

Trilobites

About 1cm long, the head is the same size as the rest of the body combined. The glabella is narrow but very convex and widens forwards. The wide, ornamented front border extends into long genal spines that may extend behind the body.

Lower-Middle Ordovician of England and North America.

The similar *Trinucleus* has a deeply furrowed glabella and is an important Ordovician zone fossil in Britain and Scandinavia.

Other similar forms from the Ordovician include *Stapeleyella*, *Omnia*, and *Tretaspis*.

66

Glossary

Aperture The main opening in the gastropod or cephalopod shell through which the animal meets the exterior.

Axis The central, longitudinal lobe of a trilobite.

Beak The convex protrusion of a brachiopod (or bivalve) valve behind (or above) the hinge.

Biconical The shape of two cones joined together at the base.

Biserial Arrangement in graptolites whereby thecae occupy both sides of a single stipe.

Brachial valve The upper, often smaller, valve of a brachiopod.

Brachidium Skeleton that supports the brachiopod lophophore.

Calcareous Made of calcium carbonate or calcite.

Calyx The body or theca of a crinoid.

Chiton/Chitinous A hard fibrous protein which makes up the hard external skeleton of insects and some other animals.

Chondrophore Attachment for shell-closing muscles in some bivalves such as *Mya* that lack hinge teeth.

Cirri Spiny outgrowths from the crinoid stem.

Convolute Style of shell coiling in which the inner whorls are partly (but not completely) obscured by the last whorl.

Crura Horn-shaped processes of the brachidium in brachiopods.

Delthyrium Part of the brachiopod pedicle valve between the pedicle foramen and the hinge. May have its own plates.

Evolute Style of shell coiling in which all the whorls are exposed.

Facial sutures Junctions between the plates on the trilobite head.

Form genus A genus used for the convenient reference of distinctive forms in cases where volutionary relationship is obscure, as is sometimes the case with plants and graptolites.

Front border Border at the front of the trilobite head.

Gape The opening in a shell opposite the hinge.

Genal angles The angles of the rear, outermost corners of the trilobite head.

Genal spines Spines that grow from the genal angles.

Genus (pl. Genera) A group of species thought to have close affinity in appearance or evolutionary relationship. The first (upper-case initial) name in a formal zoological or botanical name e.g. *Genus species*. Genera make more convenient taxonomic units than species in palaeontology.

Glabella The central, often lobed part of the trilobite head.

Interarea Part of the brachiopod shell between hinge and beak.

Involute Style of shell coiling in which the last whorl obscures all the other whorls.

Keel The outer edge of an ammonite shell.

Last whorl The main, youngest whorl of a gastropod shell, next to the aperture.

Lobe Loop in an ammonoid suture line that points backwards, i.e. away from the aperture.

Lophophore Organ of ciliated tentacles in brachiopods and some other animals.

Non-Strophic Condition of the hinge in brachiopods in which it does not occupy the width of the back edge of the brachial valve.

Pedicle The fleshy stalk of a brachiopod.

Pedicle foramen The hole in the brachiopod pedicle valve through which the pedicle protrudes.

Pedicle valve The lower and often the larger of the brachiopod valves.

Planispiral Style of coiling in which the whorls form a flat disc rather than a helical shape.

Polyp A single individual in a coral colony.

Protoconch The smallest, embryonic shell compartment or whorl in a cephalopod or gastropod shell.

Saddle Loop in an ammonoid suture line that points forwards, i.e. towards the aperture.

Septa Internal partitions in a coral cup or cephalopod shell (singular: septum).

Siliceous Made of the mineral silica, a compound of silicon and oxygen found in the spicules of some sponges.

Siphuncle The tube running through the middle of the nautiloid shell, or along one edge of the ammonoid shell, that links the compartments.

Slit band A line of ornament in some early gastropods left by the overgrowth of a slit in the edges of successive whorls.

Species A kind or type of animal or plant referred to by the second (lower-case) name in a formal zoological or botanical name e.g. *Genus species*.

Spicules Microscopic skeletal elements of a sponge.

Spire Part of the gastropod shell that excludes the last whorl.

Stipe The main stem or stalk of a graptolite.

Stratigraphy The science of ordering successive layers or strata of sedimentary rocks into a sequence that reflects relative age.

Strophic Condition of the hinge in brachiopods in which it occupies the entire width of the back edge of the brachial valve.

Suture Superficial line marking the junction of plates in the trilobite head or shell compartments in cephalopods.

Theca The cup housing a graptolite zooid; the body of a crinoid, cystoid, blastoid or (conventionally) a calcihordate echinoderm.

Thorax The trunk; the segmented part of an arthropod (and trilobite) body between the head and the tail.

Umbilicus The central hollow in the sides of a cephalopod shell or the base of a gastropod shell.

Uniserial Arrangement in graptolites whereby thecae occupy just one side of a stipe.

Valve One of the pair of shells in brachiopods or bivalves.

Venter The lower edge of an ammonoid shell below the aperture.

Zone fossil A fossil with a wide distribution but limited stratigraphic range that can, because of these attributes, be used to judge the age of the rocks in which it occurs.

Zooid An individual member of a colonial organism such as a graptolite or bryozoan.

Where fossils are found

This map outlines the basic features of European geology, illustrating the locations of the major sedimentary sequences.

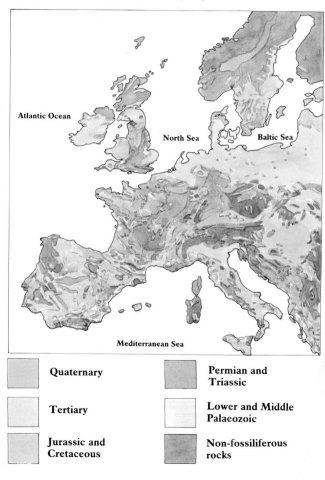

Atlantic Ocean

North Sea

Baltic Sea

Mediterranean Sea

Quaternary	Permian and Triassic
Tertiary	Lower and Middle Palaeozoic
Jurassic and Cretaceous	Non-fossiliferous rocks

RHYNIA

Psilophytales

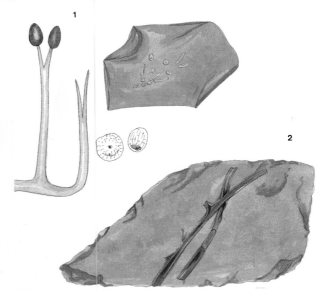

1

2

Rhynia (**1**) had prostrate, woody stems a few centimetres long from which grew branching stalks, each one terminating in a sporangium or spore capsule. Compare with *Zosterophyllum* (**2**).

Rhynia comes from the Lower Devonian of Scotland. Psilophytales ranged from the Silurian to the Devonian, although there are fossil hints of still earlier plants.

Psilophytales were the earliest definitely known land plants. They had no proper roots or leaves and probably lived on tidal flats not far from the sea.

Tiny *Cooksonia* (2–4cm tall, Silurian) is the earliest known land plant; *Zosterophyllum* (Lower Devonian) had sporangia arranged on short side-branches. Other forms include the brush-like *Asterophyllum*.

LEPIDODENDRON

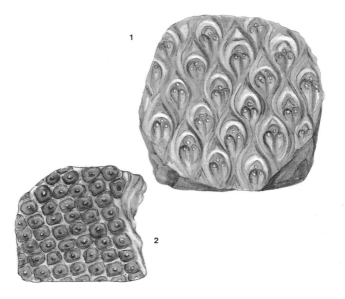

Narrow branches with needle-like leaves grew from the top of a single trunk. The bark is patterned with the lens-shaped scars of old leaf-bases (**1**), arranged spirally around the trunk.

Lower Carboniferous (Coal Measures) of Europe and North America.

Modern clubmosses such as *Selaginella* are small, but Carboniferous forms such as *Lepidodendron* grew to 30m in height and were important swamp forest trees.

The bark of the contemporary, *Sigillaria* (**2**), is patterned in straight, vertical rows of circles rather than lens-shapes. Roots of *Stigmaria* are patterned with holes arranged like the buttons in a Chesterfield sofa.

The tree-sized (up to 30m) *Calamites* stems are found as internal casts (**1**) with vertical ribbing and horizontal joints from which branches grew. *Annularia* (**2**) represents the rosettes of leaves from *Calamites* or a close relative.

Lower Carboniferous (Coal Measures) of Europe and North America.

Horsetails range from the Devonian to the small *Equisetum* of the present day. The stems are not woody, but contain pith; reproduction is from spore-bearing cones.

Several kinds of horsetails grew in the Carboniferous, known from stems, leaves and roots. *Asterophyllites* is like *Annularia* but about one-third the size.

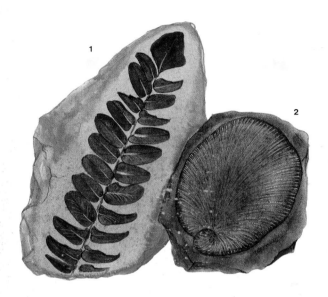

Large frond-like leaves (**1**) radiating in pairs from a central axis. *Neuropteris* is a 'form' genus, known only from its leaves.

Carboniferous (Coal Measures) of Europe and North America. Seed ferns range from the mid-Devonian to the Upper Permian.

Seed ferns looked like true ferns but were woody plants that grew to the size of large trees. Instead of spores they bore large, egg-shaped seeds.

Seed-fern and true fern fronds look so similar that it is hard to tell the difference without the seeds. *Cyclopteris* (**2**) has large, oval leaves; *Medullosa* is a commonly found seed fern. Other ferns or seed ferns include *Sphenopteris* and *Pecopteris*.

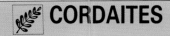

CORDAITES

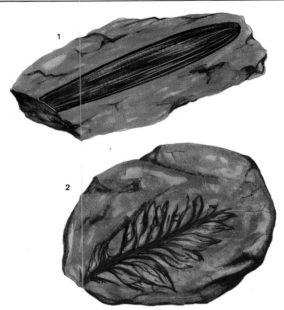

Trees with long (more than 30cm), parallel-veined ribbon- or strap-like leaves (*Cordaites*, 1) and large conifer-like cones (*Cordaianthus*, 2).

Although *Cordaites* itself is known from the Carboniferous to the Permian, the Cordaitales in general ranged from Devonian to Triassic times.

The Cordaitales bore seeds in large cones and may have included the ancestors of modern conifers.

None.

Distinctive bilobed leaves 2–5cm across, reminiscent of fig leaves.

Relatively common in Mesozoic rocks from around the world.

The Ginkgoales are related to conifers, although they are deciduous with broad leaves rather than needles. They range from the Devonian to the single living form *Ginkgo biloba*.

Several forms of Ginkgo are known. The leaves of *Ginkgo huttoni* (illustrated) from the Lower Middle Jurassic are dissected, but those of others such as *G. digitata* were fan-shaped.

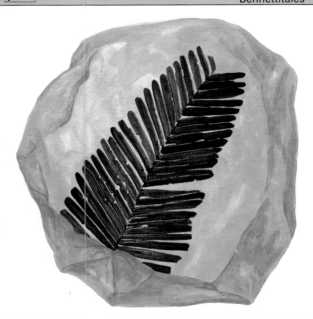

Delicate fern-like fronds. The narrow leaflets have rather square ends and are attached to a relatively broad, veined axis.

Triassic and Jurassic rocks from around the world.

Bennettitales were conifer-like trees with feathery leaves, thick cycad-like trunks and unusual flower-like reproductive organs. Range from Carboniferous to Cretaceous.

Leaves easily confused with ferns (although seed ferns such as **Neuropteris** were extinct by the Mesozoic), or the closely related seed-bearing Nilssonales (Mesozoic). The large 'flowers' look like nothing else, except possibly sea-urchin tests!

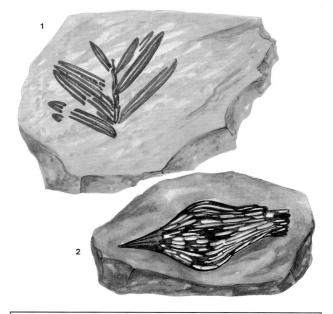

These needles of *Cephalotaxus* (**1**), 25mm long, and cone of *Doliostrobus* (**2**), 15mm tall, come from conifers of the yew family.

These specimens come from the Eocene oil shales of Messel, Germany, although conifers and their relatives are known from the Carboniferous onwards.

Other fossils include needles and cones fo the monkey-puzzle *Araucaria* (Jurassic-Recent) and the redwoods *Sequoia* (Miocene/Recent) and *Sequoiadendron* (Oligocene).

Bennettitales, cycads, cordaites (**Cordaitanthus**).

FLOWERING PLANTS
Angiosperms

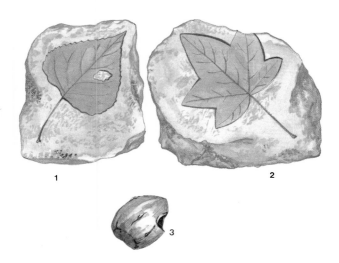

1

2

3

Leaves of poplar *Populus* (**1**, Cretaceous-Recent) and maple *Acer* (**2**, Palaeocene-Recent) are typical angiosperm remains. Pleistocene hazelnut shells (**3**, *Corylus*) show evidence of rodent gnawing.

Angiosperms are found worldwide and dominate floras from the Cretaceous onwards. Early forms such as willow and magnolia still thrive today.

The evolution of flowering plants was arguably the greatest revolution in life in the past 100 million years. Fossil leaves look little different from modern ones.

Ginkgo, some conifers.

FOSSIL WOOD

Fossil wood (such as oak *Quercus*, illustrated) is common in some places, occasionally as entire tree-trunks. It is more often found as highly polished sections in fossil shops.

Fossil wood from angiosperms is known from the Cretaceous onwards, although wood from other plants is also known.

Although the best fossil wood comes from semi-arid environments, it is known from a variety of settings such as coal swamps, peat bogs and so on.

The wood from a wide variety of plants ranging from **Lepidodendron** upwards has been found, from small fragments to whole trunks with roots attached. Perhaps the earliest examples are trunks of the enigmatic Devonian 'nematophyte' plant *Prototaxites*, up to 1m across and several metres long.

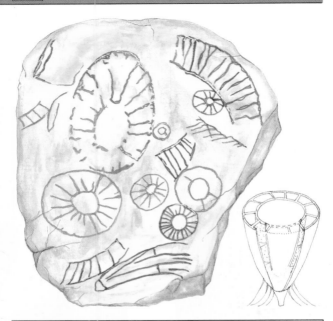

Cup-shaped (up to 10cm tall), with double walls separated by simple partitions (*Regulares*) or a complicated labyrinthine network (*Irregulares*). Often found preserved in section, as shown here.

Lower Cambrian, more rarely Middle Cambrian of Normandy, Sardinia, southern Spain, parts of north Africa, eastern Eurasia and North America.

Archaeocyaths were sponge-like marine organisms that evolved and became extinct in the Cambrian. They were the first reef-building animals.

Corals, sponges.

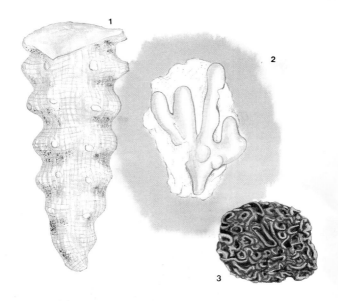

Hydnoceras (**1**, Devonian-Carboniferous) is up to 30cm tall, with criss-cross 'plaid' patterning. *Doryderma* (**2**, Carboniferous-Cretaceous) is tree-like with thick branches. *Plocoscyphia* (**3**, Cretaceous) is a complex network of tubes.

Sponges are known from 1·5 billion years ago (Precambrian) to the present day.

The variously shaped sponges are usually told apart by the microscopic, calcareous or siliceous 'spicules' that make up the skeleton — almost always the only parts preserved.

Corals, **archaeocyaths**.

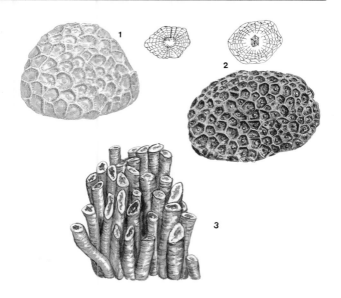

Hexagonaria (**1**, Devonian) and *Lonsdaleia* (**2**, Carboniferous) are superficially similar, massive forms with polygons left by the polyps, but differ in fine detail. Colonies of *Lithostrotion* (**3**, Carboniferous) are often bundles of tubes.

Lower Ordovician to Permian marine rocks around the world.

Rugose corals are simple, solitary or colonial, individuals often horn-shaped with six prominent and up to four subsidiary vertical internal partitions, or septa.

Scleractinian corals (only much older), *archaeocyaths* (only younger), **sponges**.

TABULATE CORALS

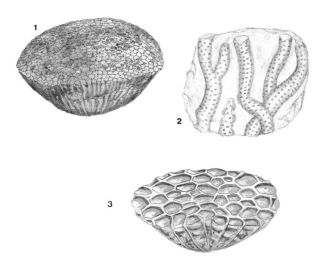

Favosites (**1**, Silurian-Devonian) is massive with tiny, boxlike spaces, but, *Coenites* (**2**, Silurian-Devonian) is often plant-like and branching. *Michelinia* (**3**, Carboniferous) has a honeycomb-like pattern.

Lower Ordovician to Permian.

The colonial tabulate corals have prominent horizontal partitions (tabulae) and weaker septa.

Other corals, sponges. Note that *Michelinia* lacks the septa prominent in rugose corals such as **Lonsdaleia** and **Hexagonaria**.

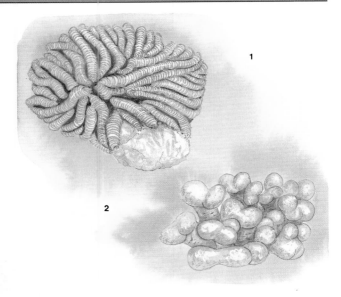

Meandrina (**1**, Eocene-Recent) is a 'brain coral', while *Porites* (**2**, Eocene-Recent) may be branching, massive or encrusting, and has small, discontinuous septa. Both are found today.

Scleractinian corals evolved in the mid-Triassic and are found in marine sediments around the world.

Solitary or colonial, scleractinian individuals have six septa, like rugose corals, but have six (as opposed to four) subsidiary septa.

Other corals, sponges.

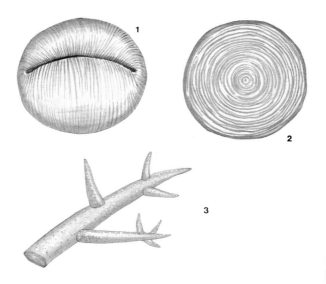

Cyclolites (**1**, Cretaceous-Eocene) is a solitary coral with many septa and a base (**2**) with concentric ridges. *Acropora* (**3**, Eocene-Recent) colonies have a delicate branched structure and are common today.

Scleractinian corals evolved in the mid-Triassic and are found in marine sediments around the world.

Solitary or colonial, scleractinian individuals have six main septa like **rugose corals** but differ in having six (as opposed to four) subsidiary septa.

Other corals, sponges.

Broad, symmetrical shell up to 8cm across, with flared aperture such that smaller whorls are almost hidden by the larger ones. The deep notch or 'slit band' in the front margin of the aperture is a typical feature.

Silurian to Triassic, worldwide.

Bellerophon was the first Palaeozoic mollusc to be described, in 1808. It is one of a group of about 70 Cambrian-Triassic molluscs distinguished by a slit band.

Tremanotus (Ordovician-Silurian); *Boiotremus*, a planispiral shell with wide aperture like a bugle.

A shell about 5cm long in which the last whorl (nearest the aperture) is very large compared with the other, tightly curled whorls.

Silurian-Permian, worldwide. A relatively common find in Devonian reef limestones.

The platyceratids included fast-growing, loosely coiled or conical shells found mainly in limestones of Ordovician-Permian age, sometimes associated with echinoderms.

Mourlonia is similar to *Platyceras* but has a less extreme aperture.

A broad shell up to 9cm long, with a low, helical spire about 7cm tall. The broad aperture has a slit near the upper edge, and the shell is heavily ornamented with bands of tubercles, grooves and growth lines.

Lower Jurassic-Lower Cretaceous.

As with the unrelated **Bellerophon**, the 'slit band' results from the closure of the slit in the edge of the aperture with the growth of the successive whorls.

None.

A smooth spherical to slightly conical shell up to 5cm tall with large last whorl and a small spire. The aperture is semicircular with a thin outer lip and a thicker inner one contiguous with the rest of the shell.

Triassic-Recent, worldwide.

The modern necklace shell is a carnivore, drilling circular holes in bivalves with the help of an acid secretion. These holes have been identified in Pliocene fossil bivalves.

None.

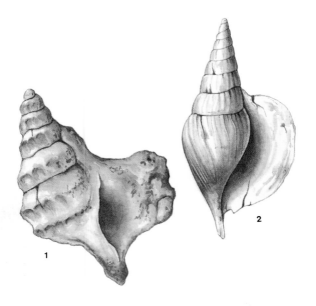

The turretted **Aporrhais** (**1**) is up to 12cm tall and heavily sculptured with a flaring aperture often extended into 'fingers'. Found worldwide in the Jurassic and Cretaceous, it is restricted to the North Atlantic today.

Hippochrenes (**2**) has a conical spire up to 8cm tall, equal in height to the width of the largest whorl. The upper lip of the aperture is fused to the spire and extended downwards into a tube. Eocene of Eurasia.

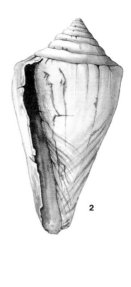

Clavilithes (**1**) is up to 15cm tall and has a robustly constructed spire with prominent shelf-like suture. The apex is sculpted but the rest of the shell is smooth. The aperture is extended downwards to form a long canal. Eocene-Pliocene, Northern Hemisphere.

Conus (**2**) is a biconical shell up to about 10cm long with a very large last whorl and a slot-like aperture that is always longer than the height of all the upper whorls combined. A carnivore that kills its prey with powerful poisons, it is known from the Upper Cretaceous to the Recent and is a useful guide fossil in the Pliocene.

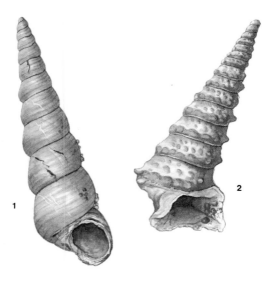

A tall, thin shell (**1**) about 5cm high and with prominent ridges spiralling round the slightly convex whorls at right angles to the growth lines. The last whorl is similar to the others and ends abruptly with an oval aperture.

Upper Cretaceous to Recent, worldwide. A useful guide fossil in the Eocene.

Several species are known today and are familiar sea-shore finds.

The turretted shape has appeared several times in evolution. Examples include the gastropods *Cerithium* (**2**, Cretaceous-Recent, which unlike *Turritella* has a slot in the aperture for a siphon); *Loxonema* (Silurian) and *Microptychia* (Carboniferous), and the ammonite ***Turrilites*** (Cretaceous).

Small (less than 5cm), smooth, deep-sutured plane spirals flat on one side and concave on the other. There may be a low spire, and occasionally both faces are concave.

Oligocene-Recent, Old World.

Although a freshwater mollusc, *Planorbis* is closely related to land snails and slugs.

None.

Tiny shells with combs of teeth on hinge lines between small, forward-pointing beaks. The shell is smooth and has faint radial ridges, with concentric growth lines becoming more prominent towards the margins.

Upper Cretaceous-Recent, worldwide.

The Common Nut Shell *Nucula nucleus* is a common seashell today.

Similar, related forms are known from the Palaeozoic, for example *Ctenodonta* (Ordovician).

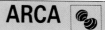
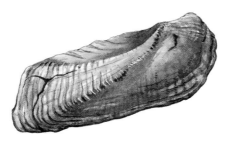

The convex shells are almost rectangular in shape with beaks displaced well towards the front and well separated from the toothed hinges. Decorated with radial ridges and a smaller number of widely spaced concentric lines.

Jurassic-Recent, worldwide.

The Noah's Ark Shell *Arca noae* is a common Mediterranean and Atlantic species today, and grows up to 8cm long.

Parallelodon (up to 15cm long, Devonian-Jurassic) has a shell of similar shape to that of *Arca* but smoother and with fewer teeth, confined to front and back ends of the long hinge.

Convex, circular about 4–5cm long with centrally placed, upward-pointing beaks. Radial ridges and fewer, more widely spaced concentric growth lines. The inside edge of the lower margin is decorated with small tubercles.

Lower Cretaceous-Recent, worldwide. The Dog Cockle.

The hinges have teeth that tend to be more slanted with increasing distance from the beak on either side.

None.

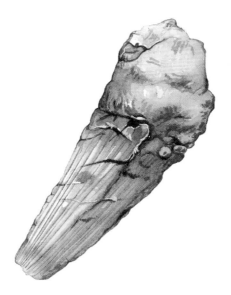

An exaggeratedly fan-shaped and triangular shell up to 25cm long. The smooth surface is punctuated with radial ridges near the pointed beak, undulating concentric ridges near the margin.

Lower Carboniferous-Recent, worldwide.

The Fan Mussel.

None; highly distinctive.

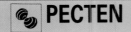

A familiar shell in which one quadrant-shaped valve is distinctly more convex than the other. The hinge is extended on either side by ear-like flanges. The shell is ornamented with broad ridges radiating from the beak.

Upper Eocene-Recent.

The Scallop.

Relatives of *Pecten* are known from the Triassic although similar shells are known from even older rocks, for example the Carboniferous form *Dunbarella*.

Up to about 15cm long. The small, flat right valve contrasts with the large, convex left valve with its overhanging beak and with its ornamentation of strong concentric growth lines and lamellae. The hinge is toothless.

Upper Triassic-Upper Jurassic. Limited to North America and Siberia in the Triassic but worldwide in the Lias. Common in Pliensbachian limestones but extinct by the Kimmeridgian.

The changing curvature of the 'Devil's Toenail' is a well-known example of evolutionary transformation.

The ornamentation is similar to that of *Ostrea.*

A variably shaped shell up to 20cm across, with small flat right valve and thick, convex left valve. The right valve is ornamented with growth lines, the left with a heavy sculpture of radial ridges and tubercles.

Triassic to Recent, worldwide.

The common oyster.

Convex left valve and flat right valve like *Gryphaea*, but less extreme.

Shell usually between 5 and 15cm tall and oval to rectangular in shape, with toothless upward-pointing beak and a long hinge line. The left valve is often more convex than the right.

Lias to Upper Cretaceous.

The distinctive species of *Inoceramus* are useful zone fossils. Some species in the chalk may be more than 1 metre long.

Ornament in *Inoceramus* varies according to species; for example, *I. concentricus* (**1**) has strong concentric ripples, whereas *I. sulcatus* (**2**) — found in some deposits such as the English mid-Cretaceous — has sharply pointed radial ridges.

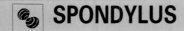

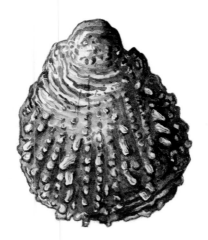

Taller (up to 12cm) than broad, oval in outline, the spiny shell surface looks like a chair after an attack by a family of kittens. It has an ornament of radial ridges of varying strength, spacing and pattern.

Lower Jurassic-Recent, worldwide.

The Thorny Oyster *S. gaederopus*.

None.

A thick, often pearly triangular shell about 5cm long decorated with concentric sausage-like ridges on the front half of each valve, weaker radial ridges on the back half, the halves separated by a prominent keel. The hinge has five teeth.

Middle Triassic to Upper Cretaceous, worldwide.

Once common, the only surviving relative is the Australasian *Neotrigonia*.

Unmistakable.

A long, narrow oval to rectangular shell between 3–15cm broad with rather flat valves and a small beak. The smooth surface may have faint concentric growth lines.

Oligocene to Recent.

The gaper shells. A spoon-shaped process or chondrophore replaces teeth inside the hinge.

Gervillella (Triassic-Cretaceous, up to 25cm) resembles *Mya* but is even longer and narrower, and is ornamented with strong concentric growth lines and has a hinge armed with long, slender teeth.

A smooth shell 15–25cm in diameter with simple suture lines. It is involute, in that the younger, outer chambers obscure the smaller, inner ones.

Oligocene to Recent.

Found nowadays in Australasian waters, the nautilus is the only modern cephalopod with an external shell, with the possible exception of females of the unrelated 'paper nautilus' *Argonauta*.

Several rather similar species are known throughout geological time, for example *Aturia* (Palaeocene-Miocene, worldwide).

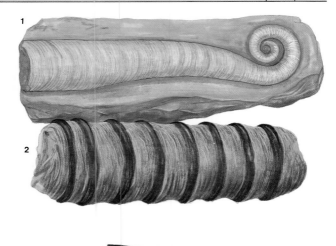

Lituites (**1**) is about 12 cm long. The shell is straight except for the end, which is coiled tightly. Middle Ordovician of Northern Europe, especially Sweden.

Dawsonoceras (**2**) from the Silurian is found as corrugated rods about 3 cm in diameter. Its relatives survived to the Triassic; the siphuncle running down the middle of the straight shells passed through a simple collar at the junction of each septum.

Bactrites (**3**) had a long, slender shell and, unusually, a siphuncle running along one edge rather than down the middle. The smallest chamber or 'protoconch' is bulbous, the whole shell looking like a sherry trumpet. The sutures were simple but with a ventral lobe. Upper Silurian to Permian of Central Europe, Sicily and Russia.

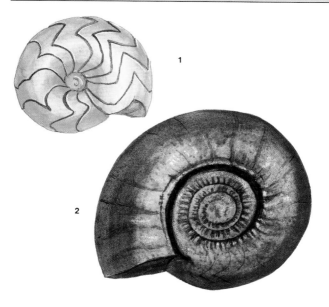

Goniatites (**1**) is about 4–5cm across, and comes from the Lower Carboniferous of England, Germany, Belgium and North Africa. The shell is thick, smooth, and involute. Suture lines have smooth lateral but zig-zag ventral lobes. Similar forms include *Tornoceras* (Middle Devonian), *Manticoceras* (Upper Devonian), *Homoceras* and *Reticuloceras* (Carboniferous).

Gastrioceras (**2**) from the Upper Carboniferous (Coal Measures) is 3–4cm across and is found worldwide. It is evolute (all whorls showing) and decorated with heavy ridges that branch and lighten towards the venter (bottom edge). The suture has curved lobes and pointed saddles.

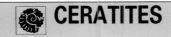

An ammonoid about 5–10cm across with a smooth convolute shell (midway between evolute and involute). The suture has simple saddles but serrated lobes.

Lower Triassic ('Muschelkalk') of Europe.

Ceratitids were widespread in the Triassic but became extinct before the end of the period.

Similar forms include *Cenoceras* (a nautiloid, rather than an ammonoid) and *Trachyceras* (Mid- to Upper Triassic).

An ammonite about 5–6cm across, evolute and flattened with a wide umbilicus, whorls squarish in section with a strong keel and ribs that curve forwards as they run towards the venter.

Early Lower Jurassic (Sinemurian), worldwide.

An excellent zone fossil for the Sinemurian.

Similar forms include the Sinemurian *Asteroceras* and *Echioceras* and the Pliensbachian *Uptonia*.

Asteroceras (1) is a stoutly built ammonite about 10cm across, with a broad umbilicus and squarish whorls like **Arnioceras** but which increase in size more rapidly towards the aperture. The lateral face bears prominent ribs and there is a strong keel with furrows on each side. The sutures are complex with pointed lobes and broad, zigzagged saddles. Sinemurian, Northern Hemisphere.

Dactylioceras (2) is about 5–10cm across, flat with a wide umbilicus and whorls circular in section. The strong ribs fork and flatten towards the venter

but meet across it, so there is no keel. Lookalikes include the Upper Bajocian *Parkinsonia* (note the narrow groove along venter) and the Toarcian **Hildoceras**.

Hildoceras (3) is an evolute shell up to 20cm across with whorls of rectangular section that increase in size rapidly towards the aperture. Strong, arching ribs on surfaces facing away from the umbilicus, and tubercles near the seam. The keel is strong with furrows on either side. The suture has broad lobes and serrated saddles. Toarcian, Old World.

A flattened, discus-shaped involute ammonite 10–15cm across with a small umbilicus and a highly complex suture pattern of pointed lobes and characteristically leaflike saddles. The surface is smooth or finely lined.

Lower Jurassic to Upper Cretaceous, worldwide.

The persistence of *Phylloceras* in the geological column is notable among the usually short-lived ammonites.

Similar forms include *Harpoceras* (Toarcian), *Tragophylloceras* (Pliensbachian) and *Leioceras* (Aalenian).

57

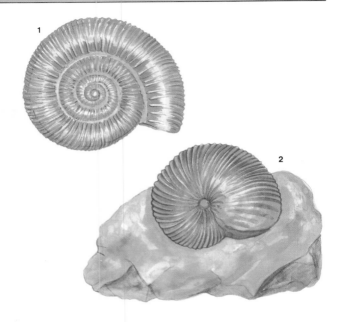

Perisphinctes (**1**) is a large, evolute ammonite (30cm across, occasionally much larger) which has deep square-section whorls with ribs that fork toward the venter. The sutures are highly complex. Middle-Upper Jurassic, Old World.

Macrocephalites (**2**) from the Lower Callovian of Europe is about 10cm across, thick, involute and decorated with many closely spaced ribs that meet across the venter. Similar forms include *Leioceras* (Aalenian) and *Clydoniceras* (Bathonian). Lower Callovian, Europe.

A convolute form about 5–10cm across, with a deep but rather narrow umbilicus and the venter sunk into a crease. Ribs radiating from tubercles on the shoulder fork forwards towards the venter.

Albian of Europe and Asia.

Hoplites is a distinctive zone fossil for the Lower part of the Albian stage.

Similar to the Middle-Upper Albian *Euhoplites*.

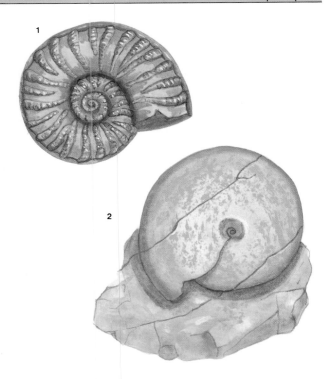

Mortoniceras (1) is flattened, evolute and about 15–25cm across, with a strong furrowed keel. Ribs originating from tubercles near shoulder and on the lateral surface run towards the venter. Albian, worldwide.

Placenticeras (2) is about 15cm across, occasionally much larger, involute with a narrow but deep umbilicus. The surface ornament is weak but the venter is extended into a blunt-edged keel framed by tubercles. Lower Cretaceous, Europe, Africa and North America.

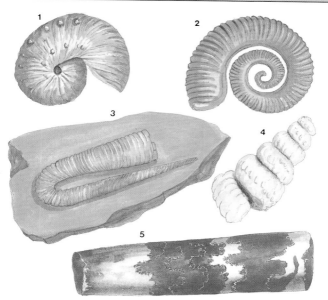

Scaphites (**1**) is an involute ammonite about 10cm across, ornamented with many fine, branching ribs. The shell is progressively more loosely coiled towards the aperture. Cenomanian, worldwide.

Crioceras (**2**) has a loose, open, ramshorn-shape. Hauterivian, worldwide.

Hamites (**3**) is a loose, open coil broadening into a shape like a curtain hook. The sutures are very complex. Albian, worldwide.

Turrilites (**4**) forms a helical spiral like the gastropod **Turritella** except that it has suture lines and an open seam between the whorls. It is also much larger, sometimes more than 30cm tall. Cretaceous, worldwide.

Baculites (**5**) is a long, straight form more than 10cm long, with complex sutures but no other ornament. It looks very like a nautiloid except that the shell is flat in section. Cretaceous, worldwide.

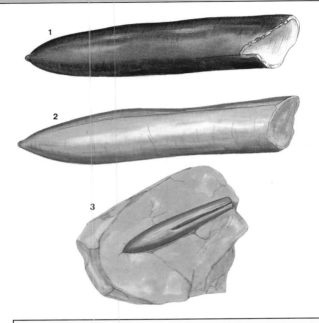

A large belemnite (**1**) about 10cm long, circular in section but with a flattened ridge running along the top surface, with grooves on either side.

Cretaceous of Europe.

The bullet-shaped belemnites (Carboniferous-Eocene) are common fossils in Jurassic and Cretaceous rocks. They are the resistant internal skeletons of squid-like animals.

Other common belemnites include *Cylindroteuthis* (**2**) (Jurassic-Cretaceous of Europe and North America), *Belemnopsis* (**3**) (Lower Jurassic of Eurasia) and *Neohibolites* (Upper Cretaceous of Europe).

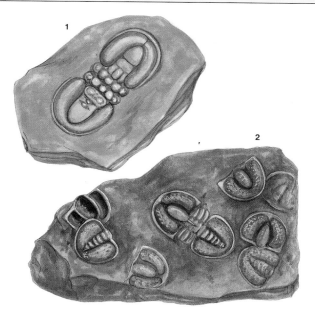

Triplagnostus (**1**) is a small (less than 1cm long), eyeless form in which the head and tail are the same size and shape. The glabella is divided into triangular front and elongate hind lobes, and there are no facial sutures. The genal angle may bear a small spine. Thorax only 2 segments, tail looks very similar to head. Similar forms include *Agnostus* (Upper Cambrian), *Condylopyge* (Middle Cambrian) and **Eodiscus** (Lower-Middle Cambrian).

Eodiscus (**2**), at less than 5mm long, is even smaller than **Triplagnostus**. The head and tail are the same size (and often found separately). The glabella has neither eyes nor facial sutures and is convex with a sharp, occasionally spiny genal angle. The thorax has 2–3 segments. The tail axis is pronounced, with strong transvere grooves. Lower-Middle Cambrian.

A spiny form about 3cm long, with a broad, semicircular head larger than the tail. The eyes are prominent and crescent-shaped. The border in front of the bulbous glabella extends into sharp genal spines. Thorax has 9 segments, tail about 6.

Lower Cambrian of Scotland and North America.

Olenellus is one of the earliest known trilobites and an important indicator ('zone fossil') for Lower Cambrian rocks, especially in Scotland and N. America.

Callavia is similar but lacks the long tail-spine and occurs in Scandinavia and in the West Midlands of England.

PARADOXIDES

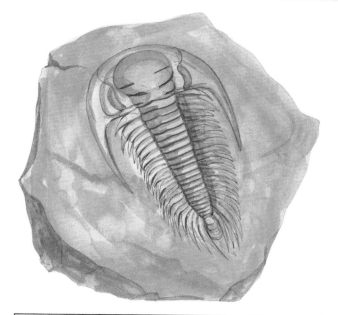

Small (2cm) to large, the head is much bigger than the tail, which may be obscured by thoracic spines. Eyes and glabella prominent, genal spines extend backwards about half the length of the body. Thorax has between 13 and 22 segments.

Important zone fossil for Middle Cambrian (St David's) rocks in Europe, North Africa and North America.

Among the largest trilobites; specimens from Bohemia may be more than 50cm long.

Similar forms include *Hydrocephalus*.

About 1cm long, the head is the same size as the rest of the body combined. The glabella is narrow but very convex and widens forwards. The wide, ornamented front border extends into long genal spines that may extend behind the body.

Lower-Middle Ordovician of England and North America.

The similar *Trinucleus* has a deeply furrowed glabella and is an important Ordovician zone fossil in Britain and Scandinavia.

Other similar forms from the Ordovician include *Stapeleyella*, *Omnia*, and *Tretaspis*.

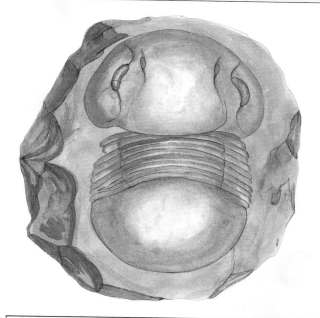

A large (5cm), smooth form in which the head and tail are the same size. The glabella, axis and genal angles are ill-defined and the fossil looks like nothing more than a giant woodlouse. The thorax has 8–10 segments.

Ordovician and Silurian of Europe.

Particularly well-known from the Ordovician of Bohemia and the Silurian Wenlock limestones of England.

The Ordovician *Illaenus* is similar but the trilobation is not quite as well-effaced as in *Bumastus*.

PHACOPS

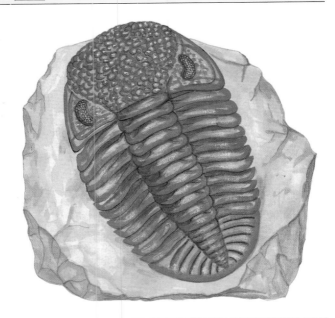

Between 3 and 8cm long, the head is much larger than the tail and has a big, ornamented glabella that broadens forward. Eyes big and kidney shaped, genal angles smooth and blunt. The thorax has about 11 segments.

Silurian and Devonian, worldwide, An important zone fossil in the Devonian.

Often found curled up into a ball like a modern woodlouse.

Similar forms iclude the Silurian *Acaste* and **Calymene**.

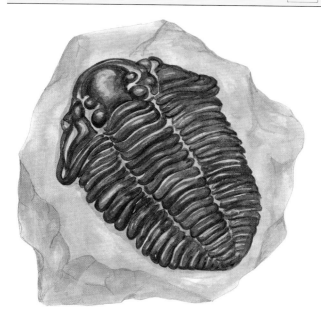

5–8cm long, the rounded tail is much smaller than the semicircular head. The glabella is swollen into 3 pairs of lobes, with a deep groove dividing it from the front edge. The eyes are large and the genal angle smooth.

Lower Silurian to Middle Devonian.

Calymene blumenbachi is well-known from Silurian (Wenlock) limestone although related species occur widely in Europe, the Americas and Australia.

Similar forms include **Phacops** as well as the Silurian *Acaste* and *Cheirurus*.

DALMANITES

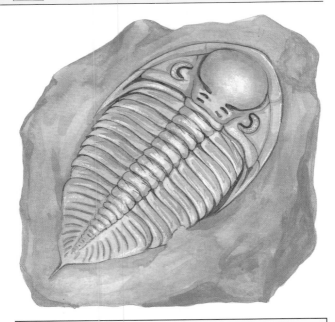

About 4cm long, the large glabella widens forwards and is cut with small transverse furrows. The thorax has 10–12 segments: the tail is the same size as the head with a smooth trailing edge extended into a long spine.

Dalmanites proeva is an important Middle Ordovician zone fossil in Europe. Other species in the genus occur in Europe, the Americas and Australia.

The lenses in the large kidney-shaped compound eyes of *Dalmanites* are often large enough to be individually visible to the naked eye or magnifying glass.

The Devonian *Odontochile* is similar.

A scorpion-like animal about 10–30cm long with six pairs of legs, the last pair developed as large swimming paddles. The abdomen terminates in a long spine.

Ordovician-Carboniferous, Eurasia and North America. *E. fischeri* is common in the Scandinavian Silurian.

Eurypterids were marine predators, related to the modern scorpions.

A length of up to 3 metres makes *Pterygotus* the largest arthropod of all time. The tail ended in a broad, flat 'fluke' and unlike *Eurypterus* it has a pair of long-stemmed pincers, each one up to 20cm long.

Barnacles are sedentary crustaceans living in conical shells made of 4–6 calcified plates. An aperture in the apex of the cone, protected by valves, allows the animal to wave its limbs in the water to breathe and catch prey.

Eocene-Recent, worldwide.

Barnacles are common everywhere today, particularly in the intertidal zone where they attach themselves to solid surfaces, occasionally in great numbers.

None.

INSECTS IN AMBER

Amber is the hardened resin of coniferous trees. Generally rare although locally abundant (for example in the Oligocene of the Baltic), it may contain the remains of insects that became trapped in the sticky resin before it solidified. Insects evolved in the Devonian and are the most abundant animals today, although their physical delicacy makes for a rather patchy fossil record.

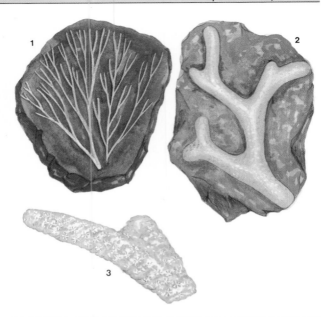

Delicate, mould-like branching networks (**1**) of thin tubes growing across rock planes.

Mainly Ordovician marine limestones, especially in Europe and North America. Trepostomes became much rarer after the Ordovician and probably died out in the Permian or Triassic.

Trepostome colonies are made of long, thin tubes joined either in a branching fashion (as here) or as massive encrustations.

Massive, coral-like forms such as *Monticulipora* (**2**). Some branching trepostomes such as *Constellaria* (**3**) have distinctive star-shaped patterns on their surfaces.

CRYPTOSTOME BRYOZOANS

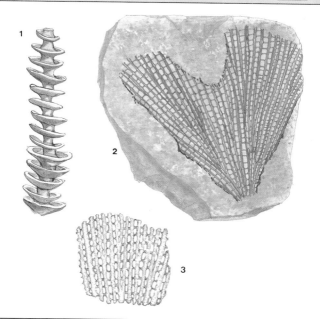

The spiral-like axis of *Archimedes* (**1**, Carboniferous-Permian) is the most easily identified bryozoan. It is sometimes found bearing lace-like sheets indistinguishable from *Fenestella* (**2**, Devonian), or *Polypora* (**3**, Ordovician-Permian).

Marine limestone of Ordovician to Permian age.

Cryptostome colonies grew erect (as in *Archimedes*), or in flat encrusting sheets.

Other bryozoans, sponges and corals.

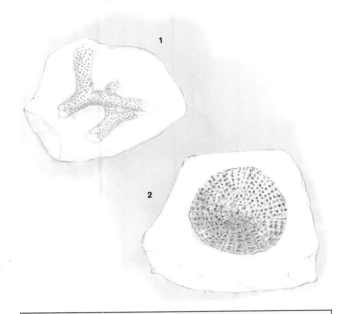

The branching cyclostome *Meliceritites* (**1**, Cretaceous) contrasts with the small (1cm) circular cheilostome *Lunulites* (**2**, Cretaceous-Eocene), with its flattened or slightly conical colonies.

Cyclostomes (Ordovician-Recent) and cheilostomes (Jurassic-Recent) include modern bryozoa. The fossils are found in marine limestones, particularly in Europe and North America.

Cyclostomes are made of simple calcareous tubes fused together to form colonies of variable shape. Cheilostomes are even more variable, with delicate, sheet-like and encrusting forms.

Encrusting cyclostomes like *Alveolaria* (Oligocene-Pliocene) and cheilostomes like *Onychocella* (Cretaceous-Recent) look very like 'brain' corals; others resemble plant stems. Examination by microscope is often the only way to find the features needed to identify bryozoa exactly.

Translucent, horny spoon-shaped shells almost equal in size, tapering towards the back.

Silurian to Recent. Found in shales often without other brachiopod species.

The modern form, found off the coasts of Japan, has changed little since the genus first appeared.

The valves of *Lingulella* (Cambrian to Middle Ordovician) are similar to those of *Lingula* but smaller (2cm long) and taper more gently towards the back. The pedicle valve has a groove for the pedicle.

***Obolella* shells** (**1**) are ovoid, calcareous and biconvex, and are typical of a few similar genera of inarticulate brachiopods confined to the Lower and Middle Cambrian.

***Orbiculoidea* shells** (**2**) are small and circular with concentric rings. The brachial valve is conical, but the pedicle valve is flat with a slot for the pedicle running from the centre to the back edge. Ordovician to Permian.

***Crania* shells** (**3**) are calcareous, ovoid and about 1cm long. The conical brachial valve lacks a pedicle and anchors directly to the substrate, which may be another brachiopod. Cretaceous-Recent.

Slightly biconvex, semicircular shell with radial ridges, 1–2cm along the straight hinge, narrow interarea but open delthyrium. The hinge is not the widest part of the shell.

Cambrian to Ordovician, worldwide.

Orthids (Lower Cambrian to Upper Permian) are rounded biconvex to plano-convex shells, strophic with open delthyria. Simple brachidium comprising a pair of crura.

Dalmanella (Ordovician-Silurian, worldwide) is circular, about 3cm across, with fine, variably spaced radial ridges and concentric ridges near the front edge. *Jivinella* from the Bohemian Lower Ordovician has a pedicle valve with a pronounced apex and coarse radial ribbing.

A nearly rectangular shell with a long hinge line across the widest part of shell (about 2cm). The pedicle valve is sharply convex, the brachial valve concave. Decorated with radial ribs and wavy concentric corrugations.

Middle Ordovician to Devonian, worldwide; a common form in the Silurian.

A member of the strophomenids (Lower Ordovician to Lower Jurassic), which with about 400 genera is the largest and most diverse brachiopod group.

None.

Strophomena (1) a semicircular, biconvex, shell in which a fold in the brachial valve is matched by a groove in the pedicle valve. Middle-Upper Ordovician.

Sowerbyella (2) a small shell (1cm across), with a concave brachial and convex pedicle valve, ornamented with fine radiating grooves. Ordovician to Lower Silurian, worldwide. Similar forms include *Aegiromena* (Middle Ordovician shales worldwide) and the large, winged shells of *Cymostrophia* from Devonian reef limestones in Europe and North America.

81

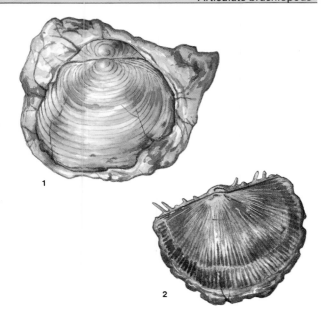

Productus (**1**) a semicircular shell about 3cm across with the hinge line across the widest part. The beak of the strongly convex pedicle valve overhangs the hinge line, but the brachial valve is flat or concave. Decorated with close-set radial ridges, concentric corrugations and the bases of spines. Carboniferous, Eurasia.

Chonetes (**2**) a semicircular, strophic shell with four long spines protruding from the hinge line. Silurian, Europe.

A smooth, oval, highly biconvex shell about 4cm long, with strongly incurved beaks overhanging a short, curved hinge line. Wide delthyrium but no interareas.

A common Silurian form worldwide.

Pentamerids (Middle Cambrian to Upper Devonian) were often highly convex with curved beaks as in *Pentamerus*, and are common in Silurian and Devonian marine shelly limestones.

Other pentamerids such as **Conchidium** and **Sieberella**.

Conchidium (1) is similar to **Pentamerus** but even more biconvex and has prominent radial ribs. With shells up to 10cm long, it is among the largest pentamerids. Silurian to Lower Devonian, often found with fossil corals in limestones of Bohemia, England and North America.

Sieberella (2) is up to 5cm long with a pedicle valve even more convex than in **Conchidium** or **Pentamerus**. The shell is smooth except for ridges that ornament a fold on the brachial valve that matches a ridged groove in the pedicle valve. Silurian-Devonian, worldwide. Similar forms include *Ivdelinia* (Lower Devonian, Europe) and *Gypidula* (Silurian to Lower Devonian), like *Sieberella* but rather smaller.

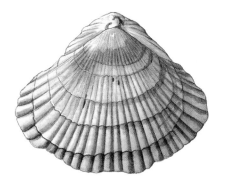

Smooth, triangular shells about 2cm long. The beak on the pedicle valve is sharp and projects above the pedicle foramen and the short, curved hinge line. A groove in the pedicle valve matches a deep fold in the brachial valve.

Characteristic of the European Middle Jurassic.

Rhynchonellids had their heyday in the Mesozoic, although they are known from the Ordovician to the present day. Shells often ribbed to give a zigzag outline to the front edge.

Similar forms include the spherical *Sphaerirhynchia* (Middle Silurian to Devonian), *Trigonorhynchia* (Silurian), *Hypothyridina* (Devonian), *Pleuropugnoides* (Carboniferous), *Tetrarhynchia* (Jurassic) and *Cyclothyris* (Cretaceous).

A 'winged' shell up to 7cm along the hinge. The pedicle valve beak is prominent with a larger interarea than on the brachial valve. A deep groove in the pedicle valve is matched by a fold in the brachial valve.

Devonian-Permian, worldwide; a useful zone fossil in the Carboniferous.

Spiriferids are known from the Middle Ordovician to the Jurassic. Their shape is variable but they tend to have a spiral-shaped brachidium and a long hinge line.

Similar forms include *Eospirifer* (Lower Devonian, Eurasia), *Cyrtospirifer* (Upper Devonian to Lower Carboniferous), *Mucrospirifer* and *Paraspirifer* (useful zone fossils in the Devonian).

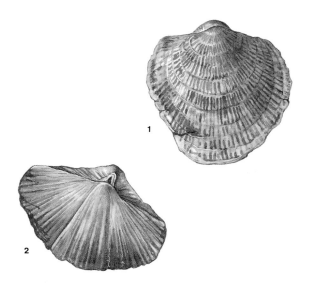

Atrypa (**1**) is longer (up to 4cm) than broad, with a convex brachial valve and a flat or slightly convex pedicle valve, in which there is a groove to accommodate a fold on the brachial valve. The ornament is a spiny meshwork of radial ridges crossed by concentric lines. Silurian-Devonian.

Cyrtia (**2**) is smooth and circular with a deep, convex pedicle valve with a very large interarea. A fold on the brachial valve fits into a groove in the pedicle valve. Silurian-Devonian, worldwide.

An oval, biconvex shell that tapers towards the beak. The hinge line is short and gently curved. Fine ribs radiate from the beak. The hole for the pedicle is large, and the delthyrium closed by small plates.

Jurassic-Recent, but a useful zone fossil in the Miocene and Pliocene.

Terebratulids are known from the Silurian to the present day, although they were at their peak in the Mesozoic. Their most characteristic feature is the large pedicle foramen.

Gryphus and *Argyrotheca* still live in the Mediterranean, whereas *Magellania* inhabits the Pacific.

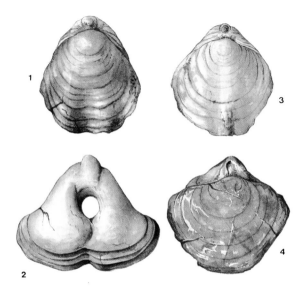

Terebratula (**1**) is up to 10cm long, smooth, biconvex and similar to **Terebratulina**. The front edge is gently crinkled, and the hinge line is curved. The pedicle foramen is large and bordered by delthyrial plates. Miocene-Pliocene.

Pygites (**2**) is a distinctive shell with a central hole caused by rapid and unequal growth rates in the shell. Jurassic. The related *Pygope* is a Jurassic-Cretaceous zone fossil and well-known from Italian marble quarries.

Sellithyris (**3**) is a smooth shell with a flattened biconvex shape and a crinkled anterior edge. Cretaceous, Europe.

Stringocephalus (**4**) spheroid shell up to 10cm across with the brachial valve more convex than the pedicle valve, which has a prominent hooked beak and pedicle foramen. Middle Devonian of Europe, and locally very abundant in shallow-water marine limestones.

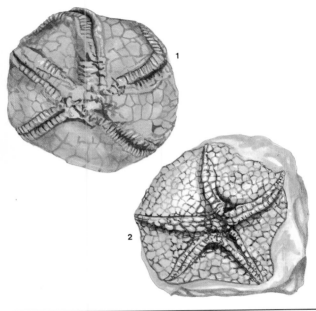

Ball-shaped body (**1**) about 2cm across wrapped with five sinuous double-rowed food grooves (four with anticlockwise twists, the other with a clockwise twist) alternating with areas of irregular plates.

Middle Ordovician of Europe and North America.

Edrioasteroids were a small group that appeared in the Lower Cambrian and died out in the Lower Carboniferous. Most known species come from Europe and North America.

Coin-sized, pentagonal *Stromatocystites* (**2**) from the Lower-Middle Cambrian of Europe has five straight, narrow food grooves and is one of the earliest known of all echinoderms.

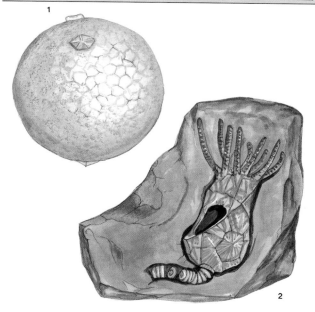

Echinosphaerites (**1**) is a flask-shaped diploporite cystoid, clothed in hexagonal plates. The triangular mouth is bordered by three knobby joints for the arms. Ordovician, Sweden and Bohemia. Similar forms include *Haplosphaeronis* and *Aristocystites*. Cystoids are found in marine sediments of Cambrian-Devonian age.

Cheirocrinus (**2**) is a rhombiferan cystoid with a regular goblet-shaped theca, a stalk and several short tentacles. Ordovician of England. Similar forms include the Silurian *Pseudocrinites* and *Lepocrinites*.

91

Rugby-ball shaped body 1–2cm tall with five prominent food grooves. Body has 13 plates arranged in three rings: 3 basals, 5 radials and 5 triangular upper plates between the food grooves.

Locally abundant in the Upper Carboniferous of Northern England.

80 genera of blastoid are known. Restricted to North America in the Silurian, they had spread worldwide by the Devonian but became extinct around the end of the Carboniferous.

The slightly larger and more angular *Orophocrinus* can be found in the same rocks as *Orbitremites*. 70 species are included in the North American genus *Pentremites*, perhaps the best-known blastoid.

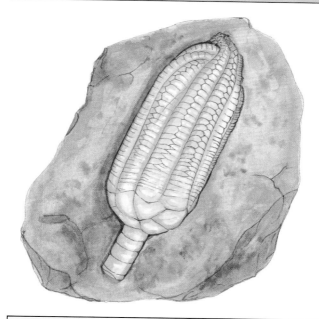

The 8cm body or calyx is much wider than tall, made from a small number of well-defined plates. The stem is stout and circular in section. The feathery arms are long, strongly plated, and often found arranged in parallel.

European Mid- and Upper Triassic, such as the shelly limestones or 'Muschelkalk' of Germany.

Encrinus was one of the last crinoids of the group Inadunata, in existence from the Lower Ordovician and comprising more then 200 species.

The similar *Dadocrinus* is often found in the same sediments.

✶ TAXOCRINUS

Crinoids

A flexible bag-like calyx 5–6cm across, made from many small plates. The arms, flexibly attached to the calyx, are long and have several branches apiece. The mouth and food grooves are exposed on the upper surface of the calyx.

Devonian to Lower Carboniferous of Europe and North America.

Taxocrinus and its relatives had a row of three 'infrabasal' plates at the base of the calyx, one plate smaller than the other two.

Sagenocrinites from the Silurian of Europe and North America has a rigidly plated calyx 8–10cm across. The arms are made from a single column of plates. Another similar form is *Protaxocrinus* from the Upper Ordovician (Ashgill).

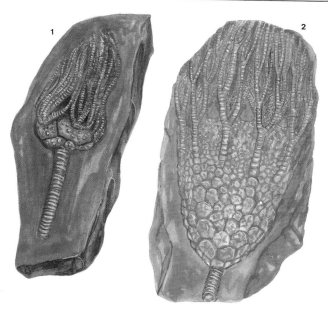

Platycrinites (**1**) has a rigid calyx 3–4cm across, made of a small number of large plates. Each feathery arm consists of two rows of plates. The stem is flat and ribbon-like. Devonian-Carboniferous, Europe and North America.

Scyphocrinites (**2**) has a calyx up to 15cm across that subsumes the lower parts of the feathery arms. The mouth and food grooves are covered by plates. The stem ends with a balloon-like float called a lobolite. A good zone fossil for the Lowest Devonian, worldwide. Similar forms include the Lower Ordovician *Reteocrinites* and the strange *Barrandeocrinus* in which the arms drooped inwards over the calyx like a wilting daisy.

95

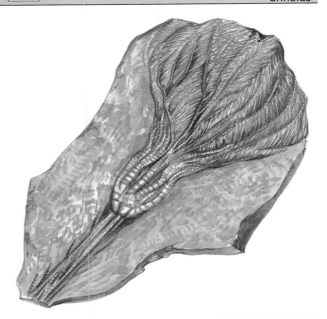

A very small, rigid calyx with long, feathery, flexible and many-branched arms. The stem is up to a metre long and may have large side-branches or cirri that grow up to envelop the calyx.

Triassic-Recent. Found as fossils in Europe and North America, and common in the English Lower Lias.

The plates of the stem in *Pentacrinites* are noteworthy for their distinctive star-shaped section.

Other crinoids, although the stem plates are unmistakeable.

Stemless, bud-shaped globular calyx 2–3cm across, made of a few large sculptured plates which are pentagonal except for a ring of hexagonal plates round the middle. The arms are rarely found.

Cretaceous (Senonian) of Europe and North America.

Marsupites is a free-living crinoid, a member of the same group that includes the modern feather-stars.

Other small crinoids, especially if found without stems or arms.

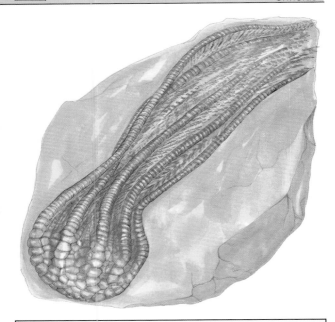

A stemless crinoid about the same size as a gooseberry. The calyx is made from many small polygonal plates. The long, strong feathery arms originate from plates near the base of the calyx.

Upper Cretaceous of Europe and North America.

A free-living crinoid, but of a very different form to the rigidly plated *Marsupites*.

Other crinoids, especially if found without stems, but the origin of the arms low on the calyx in *Uintacrinus* is a distinctive feature.

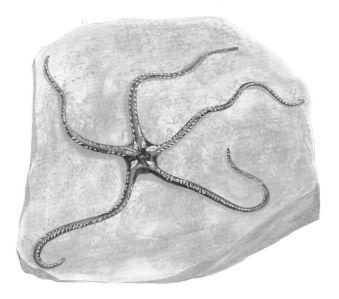

A brittle-star about 10cm across with a tiny circular to pentagonal disc and very narrow, serpentine arms.

Lower Jurassic (Lias) of Europe.

Brittle-stars have changed little in geological time. The Ordovician (Ashgill) *Lapworthura* looks much the same as the living *Ophiura*.

Similar forms include *Encrinaster* with its long, narrow-tipped arms and pentagonal disc. Upper Ordovician to Lower Carboniferous of Europe, especially the Lower Devonian Hunsrück shales of Germany.

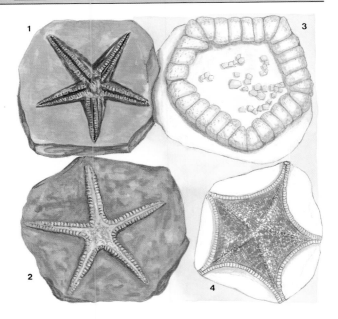

Salteraster (**1**) is a true starfish 4–5cm across. The large marginal plates on the broad, strong arms are separated from the dorsal plates by ribbons of flexible integument. Middle Ordovician to Silurian of Europe and North America. The similar *Siluraster* comes from the Ordovician of Britain and Bohemia.

Pentasteria (**2**) is a true starfish, 8–10cm across with a small body and narrow, straight arms with large plates on the margins and smaller inner plates. Jurassic-Eocene, Europe.

Metopaster (**3**) is a pentagon 3–4cm across with extremely short arms but very prominent marginal plates. Upper Cretaceous (Maastrichtian).

Calliderma (**4**), 10–15cm across, has a large body grading into short arms. Cretaceous-Oligocene, Europe.

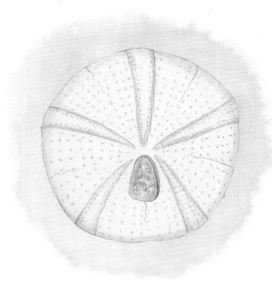
A sea-urchin with a rounded to pentagonal test about 6cm across and 2–3cm tall. There is a distinctive anal groove on the top surface.

Jurassic-Cretaceous of Europe; common in the Bajocian (Middle Jurassic) of England.

Fossils may show small circular marks that are the remnants of spine-bases.

The Jurassic sea-urchin *Pedina* is similar except that the anus is less prominent.

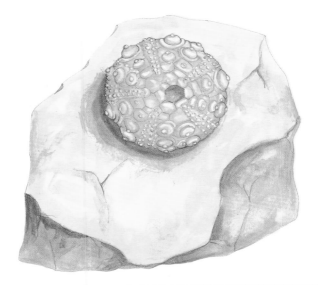

A sea-urchin with a flattened test about 2cm in diameter. Spine bases are prominent and warty, each one with a circle of smaller tubercles around the base.

Jurassic-Cretaceous of Europe.

Although the presence of spines is evident in *Acrosalenia* and other echinoids, they are shed after death and found only rarely as fossils.

Hemicidaris is slightly larger (3–4cm), with a large mouth with notches around the edge, food grooves more sinuous and less well-defined than in *Acrosalenia*. Each spine-base tubercle has a circle of holes just below the tip.

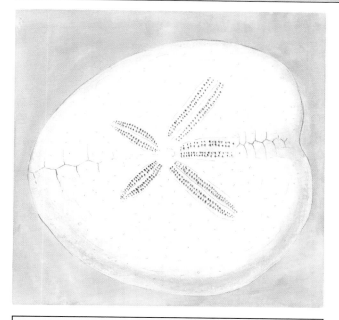

A heart urchin 4–6cm long and 3–4cm tall. The mouth is in the cleft at the top of the 'heart' protected by a lower 'lip'. The anus (at the other end) forms a swelling on the lower surface.

Cretaceous (Cenomanian) to Palaeocene worldwide. Especially well-known from Upper Cretaceous (Turonian-Senonian) of England and France.

Studies of the changes in shape in *Micraster* mapped through the Upper Cretaceous have revealed one of the classic case histories of evolution in action.

A similar form is *Holaster* from the Jurassic and Cretaceous, in which the heart shape is not as marked as in *Micraster*.

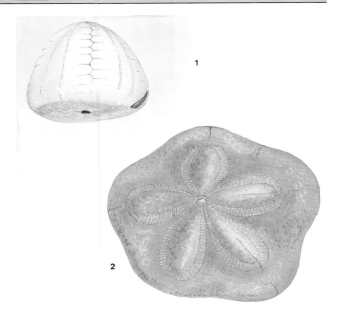

Conulus (1) is 4cm across, 3–4cm tall. Round in outline (although not perfectly circular), hemispherical to conical in side view. The mouth lies directly underneath the tall apex, with the anus on one edge. Cretaceous of the Northern Hemisphere, common in the English chalk (Senonian).

Clypeaster (2) is a flattened oval 11–12cm long with broad, petal-shaped food grooves in the centre of the upper surface. The lower surface is flat or convex with the mouth in the centre and the anus on one edge. Eocene-Recent, worldwide; some species are useful Tertiary zone fossils. Similar forms include the Middle Jurassic **Nucleolites**, about the same size and shape except that the food grooves run all the way round the test.

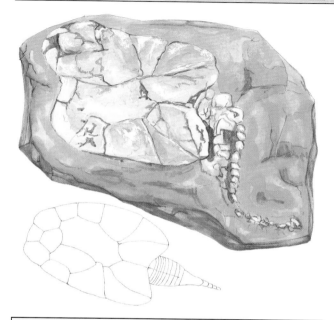

Flattened echinoderm-like form with a distinct plated 'head' and short, segmented 'tail'. The plates on the upper surface are larger than those on the lower surface. More often found as fragments.

Locally abundant in Ordovician shales of Brittany and Bohemia.

The irregular calcichordates occur in marine rocks from the Cambrian to the Devonian. Some scientists think that they are more closely related to vertebrates than echinoderms.

Mitrocystites (Ordovician, Bohemia); *Placocystites* (Silurian, England); *Cothurnocystis* (Ordovician, Scotland); *Ceratocystis* (Cambrian, Bohemia).

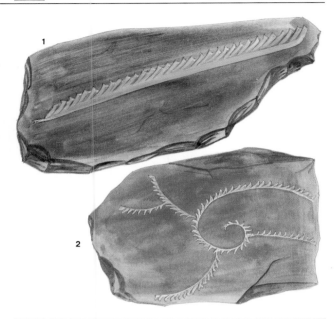

Monograptus (**1**) A uniserial graptoloid form with thecae arranged along just one edge of the blade like hacksaw teeth. Colonies can be long and straight or arranged in graceful coils, and the thecal shape is similarly varied.

Llandovery to Lower Devonian of Europe.

The various forms of *Monograptus* are extremely useful as zone fossils in the Silurian.

Rastrites (Llandovery) has long, projecting thecae; *Cyrtograptus* (**2**; Wenlock, worldwide) is a beautiful uniserial graptolite with branches thrown at regular intervals from the spiral main stem.

TETRAGRAPTUS

Tetragraptus (**1**) is a graptolite with four uniserial fretsaw-like blades arranged in various ways according to the species, but always meeting at a central apex.

Lower Ordovician (Arenig-Llanvirn), worldwide.

As with *Monograptus*, species of *Tetragraptus* can be useful as zone fossils.

Phyllograptus (**2**; Lower Ordovician, worldwide) is made of four separate blades as in *Tetragraptus* but fused together back-to-back. The four blades (at right angles to one another) are usually only seen in specimens preserved in three dimensions.

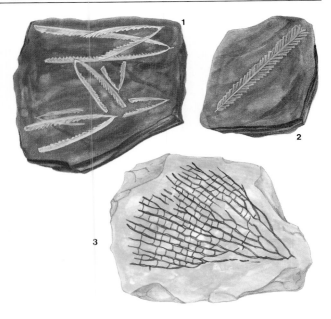

Didymograptus (**1**), a graptolite with two uniserial branches, sometimes resembling a tuning fork in shape. Ordovician (Arenig-Carodoc), worldwide.

Diplograptus (**2**), leaf-like colonies with thecae facing outwards on both sides of the blade. Ordovician-Silurian (Llanvirn-Llandovery), worldwide. Similar forms include *Orthograptus* (Upper Ordovician to Lower Silurian) and *Climacograptus* (Arenig-Landovery).

Dictyonema (**3**) is a finely branching fan-like form with strong cross-branches between the main branches. Unlike most graptolites, which floated freely near the surface of the sea, the colonies of *Dictyonema* and its relatives were rooted to the seafloor. Middle Cambrian-Carboniferous, worldwide. Similar forms include *Rhabdinopora* (Tremadoc) although it may be confused with the bryozoan *Fenestella*.

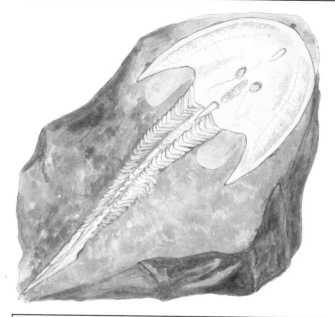

An armoured fish 10–20cm long with a broad, semicircular head, paddle-shaped fins behind and a slender, heavily armoured tail. Usually only isolated plates and scales are found.

Silurian-Devonian of Eurasia and North America.

Ancient relatives of the modern lamprey, many different kinds of jawless fishes are known from the Upper Cambrian to the Devonian.

Cephalaspis itself is fairly distinctive if found complete, but fragments may be confused with other forms such as *Pteraspis* (Silurian-Devonian).

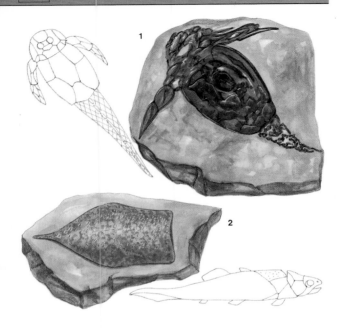

Pterichthyodes (**1**) A fish about 20cm long with a heavy, box-like suit of armour and a scaly tail. The underside of the head armour is flat, but the upper surface is arched. Middle Devonian freshwater deposits, especially abundant in northern Scotland. Similar forms include *Bothriolepis* (Upper Devonian), armoured but with naked hindparts, the mid-Devonian *Asterolepis* and the unrelated *Cephalaspis*.

Coccosteus (**2**) A fish about 20cm long with heavy body armour smoother in outline than in *Pterichthyodes* and more clearly divided into head and trunk sections. Another fish characteristic of the Middle Devonian of Scotland, although a number of highly varied relatives are known from the Upper Devonian of Germany.

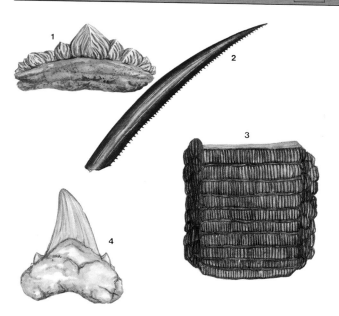

Tooth of **Hybodus** (**1**). *Hybodus* represented a group of sharks common between the Triassic and Cretaceous. Their long (about 20cm), fluted spines (**2**) were used to support the fins. Worldwide.

Myliobatis (**3**). A ray with large batteries of teeth used for crushing shellfish. Cretaceous-Pliocene, worldwide, Shell-crushers from the Cretaceous shark *Ptychodus* have a distinctive, finger-print-like pattern of ridges.

The teeth of the shark **Lamna** (**4**) can be recognized by the two small accessory toothlets on either side of the pointed, main tooth. The large teeth of the great white shark *Carcharodon*, likewise known from Tertiary rocks around the world, are triangular and serrated without extra toothlets.

111

A deep-bodied ray-finned fish about 25cm long with a small mouth well-armed with stout peg-like teeth. The thick and shiny scales are square to rectangular or rhomboidal in shape.

Lower Jurassic (Lias), familiar from Lyme Regis is Dorset, England.

Dapedium is a very early member of a group of fishes now almost entirely extinct, but for the heavily armoured garpike *Lepisosteus*, the bowfin *Amia* and a few other forms.

The deep-bodied form has evolved many times in the history of fishes. Other examples include *Amphicentrum* (Carboniferous), *Cleithrolepis* (Triassic) and *Microdon* (Jurassic).

A small fish 10–20cm with heavy scale armour. Often found complete or nearly so, *Osteolepis* and its close relatives have distinctive large scales or scutes on each side of the fin bases. fin bases.

Middle Devonian of northern Scotland. Similar forms are known from the Devonian of Europe, Canada, Spitzbergen, Greenland and Australia.

Osteolepis is a member of a group of lobe-finned fishes ancestral to the first amphibians, which appeared in the Upper Devonian.

Similar forms include *Gyroptychius*, *Thursius*, *Glyptolepis* and the lungfish *Dipterus*.

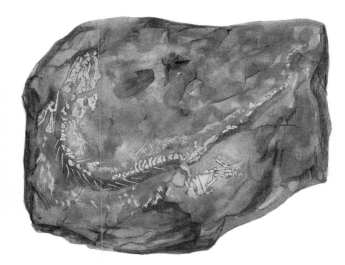

A lizard-like animal about 20cm long with a small head, well-developed fore- and hindlimbs and a long, sinuous tail.

Lower Carboniferous. So far known only from a single site at East Kirkton in southern Scotland.

Besides *Westlothiana*, affectionately known as 'Lizzie', East Kirkton has yielded fossils of amphibians and arthropods, opening a unique window on the Lower Carboniferous.

Easily confused with the many contemporary species of Lower Carboniferous amphibian.

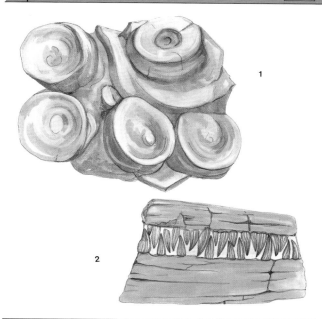

The vertebrae (1) of these marine reptiles are circular, about 8cm across (although size is extremely variable), slightly concave on each side and rather featureless except for swellings on the edges where other bones joined.

Mesozoic, worldwide. The English Lias is noted for its ichthyosaur remains.

Ichthyosaurs were important marine reptiles that occupied the same ecological niche that dolphins and porpoises do today. Their pointed teeth (2) had deeply furrowed crowns.

Vertebrae can be mistaken for those of other marine reptiles such as plesiosaurs. Large, pointed teeth (10cm long) found isolated in Mesozoic sediments may come from large carnivorous plesiosaurs called pliosaurs.

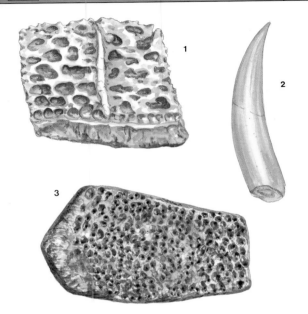

Crocodiles are betrayed as fossils by the square or rectangular bony plates (**1**) that formed their body armour. The honeycomb-like pitting on the top surfaces give them a resemblance not dissimilar to waffles.

Triassic-Recent, worldwide.

The pointed, curved and deeply rooted teeth (**2**) are also commonly found as fossils although their variation in size — even in one jaw — make them hard to identify to species.

The pitted, bony plates or 'scutes' of crocodiles may be confused with the large, trapezium-shaped or rectangular scutes of tortoises such as *Trionyx* (Triassic-Recent, Old World) (**3**).

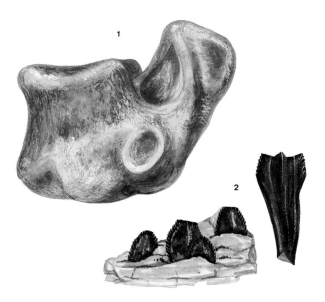

Isolated bones such as this vertebra (**1**) and tall, flat-topped teeth (**2**) are mostly all that remains of the large plant-eating dinosaur *Iguanodon*.

Lower Cretaceous of Europe (Neocomian) of western North America and Eastern Asia.

The first dinosaur to be described scientifically. Although the first known specimens were fragments, whole skeletons have been found in a mineshaft at Bernissart in Belgium.

Most dinosaur specimens are found as small fragments of bones or teeth that may need specialized assistance for sure identification. The teeth of herbivores like *Iguanodon*, though, are easily distinguishable from the curved, serrated teeth of carnivores such as *Megalosaurus*.

An unusual 10m-long dinosaur with a large, flat crocodile-like head full of sharp teeth and impressive 30cm scimitar-like claws on its forefeet. It is thought to have dined on fish.

Lower Cretaceous, England.

The first specimen was discovered by chance by an enthusiast out walking his dog — proof that great fossils await discovery by the amateur.

Similar forms may occur in the Cretaceous of West Africa.

Dinosaur eggs are usually found as fragments and are difficult to identify. Very occasionally, entire buried nests of the eggs, looking like very old, dried potatoes, are found in circular or linear arrangements.

Mesozoic, especially Upper Cretaceous sediments of southern France and Transylvania.

The species of dinosaur that laid any particular egg is of course impossible to determine, but a favourite candidate for French eggs is the large plant-eating dinosaur *Hypselosaurus*.

None.

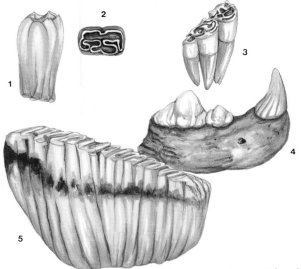

Equus; horse molars (**1**) are tall and rather square in section, with a distinctive pattern of loops and contours when seen in top view (**2**). Pleistocene river gravels.

Bison; the lower molars (**3**) of the steppe bison *Bison priscus* are tall and blade-like; the upper teeth are more blocky in appearance. The teeth of the extinct wild cattle *Bos primigenius* look very similar, but have taller crowns. Both are found in Pleistocene river gravels and cave sites.

Crocuta; cave hyena canines (**4**) have a distinctive, pointed shape. Teeth of bear *Ursus* are similar in shape but larger. Mostly found in ancient 'hyena dens' in caves, where they can occur in abundance.

Mammuthus; the numerous and close-packed enamel ridges of the huge, heavy teeth of the woolly mammoth (**5**) help to distinguish the teeth from those of related elephants such as *Palaeoloxodon* and *Archidiskodon*, which have fewer ridges, more widely spaced. Found in glacial and river gravels, and even occasionally dredged up from the North Sea in fishing nets!

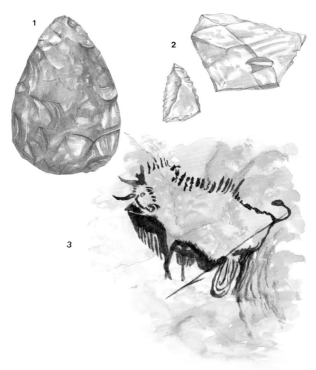

Acheulean hand-axe (**1**), the classic stone tool. Invented by *Homo erectus*, this Swiss Army Knife of the stone age remained part of the human toolkit for more than 500,000 years.

Mousterian flakes and scraper (**2**) represent the culture of Neanderthal Man (*Homo sapiens neanderthalensis*) in western Europe.

Cave paintings (**3**), such as this bison are rare but telling evidence for the arrival of *Homo sapiens* in Europe. The most famous cave paintings including this one are at Lascaux in the Dordogne valley in south-west France.

Index and checklist

All species in Roman type are illustrated.
Keep a record of your sightings by ticking the boxes.

ILLUSTRATED GLOSSARY

AMMONOID

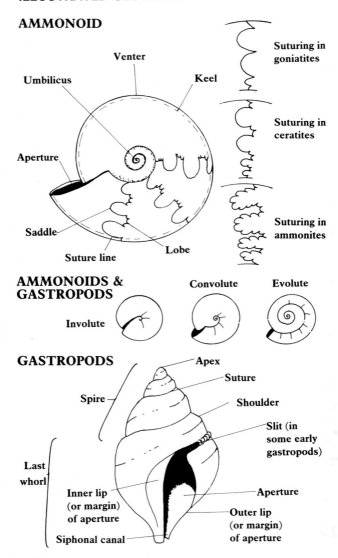

Venter

Umbilicus

Keel

Aperture

Saddle

Suture line

Lobe

Suturing in goniatites

Suturing in ceratites

Suturing in ammonites

AMMONOIDS & GASTROPODS

Involute

Convolute

Evolute

GASTROPODS

Apex

Suture

Spire

Shoulder

Slit (in some early gastropods)

Last whorl

Inner lip (or margin) of aperture

Aperture

Outer lip (or margin) of aperture

Siphonal canal